The Whippingham Papers

THE WHIPPINGHAM PAPERS

WORDSWORTH CLASSICS

The paper in this book is produced from pure wood pulp, without the use of chlorine or any other substance harmful to the environment. The energy used in its production consists almost entirely of hydroelectricity and heat generated from waste material, thereby conserving fossil fuels and contributing little to the greenhouse effect.

This edition published 1995 by
Wordsworth Editions Limited
Cumberland House, Crib Street
Ware, Hertfordshire SG12 9ET

ISBN 1 85326 611 6

Typeset in the UK by Antony Gray
Printed and bound in Denmark by Nørhaven

❧❦❧

Contents

Preface

New words are needed to explain the object of the present volume.

No propensity to which human nature is addicted, or lech to which it is prone, holds firmer root than flagellation. Moreover, the interest in the rod is not confined to those who actually use it, either actively or passively, as is amply proved by the literature on the subject.

Attempts, partial and by no means exhaustive, have lately been made to codify some of the numerous books which the birch has called into existence. We allude to that noteworthy set of bibliographia: *Index Librorum Prohibitorum*, 1887; *Centuria Librorum Absconditorum*, 1879; and *Catena Librorum Tacendorum*, 1885.

The following extract from one of the works in question will serve to explain our meaning:

> The propensity which the English most cherish is undoubtedly flagellation. That the rod has been used in all Roman Catholic countries by the priests as an

instrument to serve their own lubricity is, of course, not to be denied; and although the subject has been most seriously and scientifically treated by a Dutch doctor, yet this vice has certainly struck deeper root in England than elsewhere.

Books innumerable in the English language are devoted to this subject alone; and numerous separate plates exist depicting whipping scenes; it has caused the separation of man and wife; the genteelest female schools have been made subservient to the passions of its votaries; and formerly it was spoken of without reserve on the public stage. Flagellation anecdotes frequently occur in the pages of *The Rambler's*, *The Original Rambler's*, *The Bon Ton* and other similar magazines. *Notes and Queries* contains many communications on the subject. Only a few years back a remarkable and lengthened correspondence filled the columns of such domestic periodicals as *The Family Herald*, *The Englishwoman's Domestic Magazine*, &c., the pith of which was collected and issued in a volume entitled *Experiences of Flagellation*, 1885. That the topic has not lost its interest with the present generation may be estimated by the rapidity with which the first edition of this work was sold.

At the early part of this century very sumptuously fitted up establishments, exclusively devoted to the administration of the birch, were not uncommon in London; and many women served, as it were, an apprenticeship in order to acquire the art of gracefully and effectively administering the rod.

The papers contained in the present volume are of a varied character – act and fiction, poetry and prose alternately occupy its pages – so that every class of reader will, we trust, find something to his liking. Several of the tales and many of the poetic effusions are from the pen of the 'Expert' whose *Romance of Chastisement* caused so much sensation seventeen years ago. That remarkable book, it will be remembered, was never completed by the publisher, although the author had done his task. The MS then laid aside, having fortunately fallen into our hands, we have utilised it to a great extent in the following pages.

The remaining pieces speak for themselves, and illustrate more thoroughly, perhaps, than any other collection of the same scope the ever interesting subject of flagellation.

Can you not give us something from a source
    Other and brighter than the tear-fraught Rod?
We give a promise to be good perforce —
    Still, if the captious critic will but nod
Like Homer who, asleep, was good of course,
    We'll try; the exception shall at least be odd:
The ocean billows, as they homeward roll
    In smooth monotony, shall raise the SOLE.

Arthur's Flogging

Oh Birch! thou common dread and doom of all boys,
  Who found out first thy properties of pain?
Who gave thy tough lithe twigs their power to appal boys?
  Who laid the red foundations of thy reign?
Who made thee haunt by night the dreams of small boys?
  Who gave thee power o'er us thy trembling train?
Who made thee master of our bums, and lord?
Who flogged boys first? and what flogged boy first
    roared?

No tongue there is to say, no soul to know it;
  In blood and tears were laid thy first foundations,
But by whose hand who knows, and who can show it?
  So long the rod has ruled boys of all nations.
Oh, Birch! accept a schoolboy for thy poet,
  Whose bum has blushed from frequent flagellations
These three years past; thou knowest it, Birch, and more;
And while I write is not my bottom sore?

Oh, Birch! whose mouth should sing thee if not mine?
   Is there a schoolboy oftener flogged than I am?
Have I not marks upon me still of thine?
   Is there a boy, I say, from here to Siam,
Between the ages of eighteen and nine,
   Or has there been a boy since the age of Priam,
In days unknown of or in years unsearched,
Who has been oftener or more soundly birched?

Right well thou knowest the voice that now invokes
   Thine oft experienced aid and inspiration;
By all the rods I have felt, and all their strokes,
   By all the burning pangs of my probation;
By the salt brine in which thy keeper soaks
   Thy twigs to make them fit for flagellation,
By their green buds that make one hate the spring,
By all their suppleness and all their sting;

By all the scars I ever took behind,
   By all the cuts thou has ever given me, since
At my first flogging, still I keep in mind,
   The first cut made my young posteriors wince;
By thy full power on boys of every kind,
   Alike on smarting page and tingling prince;
By all my floggings, whereso'er I got 'em;
By all the weals upon my naked bottom;

By all the blood of mine that thou hast shed,
   And all the blood of all my schoolfellows,
And all that ever made the birch twigs red,
   From tender bottoms blushing like a rose;
By all the boyish bums that ever bled,
   Or ever will bleed from thy backside blows,
As long as supple twig and swelling bud
Make high-born bottoms 'blush with noble blood'.

For, as all schoolboys know, the birch, like God,
   Has no respect of persons; all that come
Within the rule and reach of the red rod,
   Are equal in the rod's sight, all and some;
Down go all breeches at the master's nod,
   No preference shown of bum to blushing bum;
The birch still red with blood of his inferiors,
May flog the far descended boys posteriors.

Yes, birch is democratic; for my part,
   When on the flogging block, I've often wished
To be a boy that drives a plough or cart
   By fields and streams where once I rode and fished;
If when we're flogged birch did not make us smart
   As it makes me smart every time I'm swished,
It were worth while to boast of long descent
If it could save our skins from detriment.

But crests and arms and quarterings and supporters,
   And all emblazoned flourishes her field,
Are no defence for a boy's hinder quarters,
   Nor will he find his coat of arms a shield
For his bare bottom, when, like other martyrs,
   He writhes beneath the birch that leaves him wealed
All over his red quivering nether parts,
And smarts and roars, or only sobs and smarts.

His coat is birch *per fesse*, and total gules,
   Poor fellow! 'tis an ancient coat, and good;
And, from of old, was borne in all boys' schools
   Since the first flogging block was made of wood;
All dunces, truants, rebels, idlers, fools,
   That e'er were birched have dyed it with their blood;
I too have often borne it. I, thy poet,
Thou knowest, Oh, Birch! and my posteriors know it.

Thou knowest my floggings, when and where I got 'em,
   How I was flogged, how often, and what for;
Though I myself have in great part forgot 'em,
   Now that the marks are on my flesh no more;
Thou knowest the new marks fresh upon my bottom,
   All the scars, cuts, and weals that make it sore,
All the red ridges, all the parts half healed,
Since last my bottom gave thee a fair field.

By all these tokens, and each smarting sign,
   Birch! hear once more a flogged boy's invocation,
Who never in his life had less than nine,
   And never skulked or shirked his flagellation,
And never came off without marks of thine
   To show for days in written indication;
He must have been well swished the day he got 'em,
To bear in sign of birch on his bare bottom

I sing of Arthur's Flogging; I, who heard
   The boy himself sing out beneath the birch,
Louder and shriller than a singing bird,
   Or screaming parrot on its gilded perch;
He has had this week three floggings; this, the third,
   A good sound swishing, was for missing church.
And on this point no two boys ever differed,
That no boy gets more flogged than Arthur Clifford.

The time was noon; the flogging room the scene;
   And all the boys in Arthur's form were there;
And in they brought the culprit of thirteen,
   A boy with bright dark eyes and bright gold hair,
Of slender figure and of careless mien,
   Though now his flushed face wore a cloud of care,
And with eyes downcast like a shrinking girl's,
He came on blushing right up to his curls.

To him the doctor, in judicial wise,
  'What kept you, Clifford Minor, out of church?'
Then the boy lifted his dark violet eyes,
  And saw the flogging block, and saw the birch,
And felt the blood to cheeks and forehead rise,
  And wistfully looked round him as in search
Of any pretext to ward off his fate,
And answered boldly, 'Please, sir, I was late.'

'What made you late, sir?' with a smile and frown
  Of outward wrath and cruel inward joy,
Replied the master, 'Were you not up town
  On some vain errand for some foolish boy?'
No answer. 'Clifford, take your trousers down.'
  With piteous eyes uplifted, the poor boy
Just faltered, 'Please, sir,' and could get no farther.
Again, that voice, 'Take down your trousers, Arthur.'

Then smiles were seen on many small boys' faces,
  And smothered laughs on many a big boy's lips,
With stifled whispers and subdued grimaces,
  While Arthur, with cold trembling finger tips,
Stood fumbling at his waistband and his braces,
  Then bared the fleshy parts about his hips,
And let his trousers fall about his heels,
And showed a pair of buttocks full of weals

A pretty pair of buttocks, round and plump,
  With red points here and there, that seemed to dot
  'em,
And here and there a broken twig or stump
  Of birch still sticking in the flesh to spot 'em;
And many a red ridge right across the rump,
  And many a half-healed scar on Arthur's bottom;
There might you see in fair and open fight
The red rose making war upon the white

So with his parti-coloured bottom bare,
  With all its wounds for all the school to mock,
With naked haunches delicately fair,
  The parts unscarred as white as lady's smock,
A boy with violet eyes and yellow hair
  Knelt, with his shirt up, on the flogging block;
And o'er him stood his master, fresh from church,
With a long, strong, lithe, new, green, sappy birch.

Once – twice – he whirled it whistling round his head,
  Then struck with all a strong man's utmost might,
And Author's bottom blushed one burning red
  All over, not an inch was left of white,
And from a score of weals at once it bled,
  Great tingling weals that sprang up left and right
Under the birch, and from them every one
The drops of blood as thick as raindrops spun.

And all the cuts his bottom had before,
　　The parts where bits of birch were sticking still
Like spearheads in the wounds they had made of yore,
　　When last the birch had all its cruel will,
Began to bleed afresh and smart once more
　　As sheer through the air the whistling twigs swept
　　　shrill,
There, they're very sharp and straight, and smote afresh
The tingling space of naked quivering flesh.

The first cut made the flogged boy flinch and start,
　　And from his lips pain forced a short sharp cry,
So hard it fell on such a tender part,
　　Still sore from floggings felt so recently;
Right through his flesh he felt the bitter smart,
　　Like a snake's sting down darted from on high,
And writhed, and roared out at the second blow –
'Oh! please, sir; oh! sir! Oh! oh! oh! oh! oh!'

Swift as the birch on Arthur's bottom fell,
　　Hard as the birch on Arthur's bottom rung,
Like the deep notes of a funeral bell,
　　The master's words of keen rebuke were flung,
'I'll flog you well for crying – flog you well;
　　I'll have no crying here, boy; hold your tongue;
I'll give you more to cry for, you young dog, you!
I'll flog you – flog you – flog, flog, flog, flog, flog you.'

At every pause, at every word, a blow
   Fell, and made Arthur's bottom smart and bleed.
'Take that, sir,' 'Oh! sir, please, it hurts me so;
   You don't know how you hurt me, sir, indeed;
Oh! sir, I'll never – Oh! sir, please, sir, Oh!'
   And many a blood flake like a crimson bead,
At each fresh cut showed where each twig or bud
Had fallen, and drawn its one drop more of blood.

At each cut, Arthur, while his hands were free,
   Pulled down his shirt and rubbed his bottom; but
Though some relief from torture it might be,
   The gate of mercy was that instant shut;
And Arthur felt all through, but could not see,
   How hard the doctor laid on the next cut,
And as the sharp twigs were afresh applied,
Fresh blood ran from fresh weals on his backside.

And over him in front stood Philip Shirley
   And Edward Beauchamp, holding up his shirt;
And if he plucked it from them, they looked surly,
   As they drew up again the blood-stained skirt,
And shook their fists aside at Arthur's curly
   Head, or else grinned, and whispered, 'Does it hurt?'
And only held the spotted shirt up higher,
Till the birch seemed to set his bum on fire.

He clapped his hands behind – the birch twigs
    caught 'em
  Across, and made them tingle too and bleed;
And harder still the birch fell on his bottom,
  And left some fresh red letters there to read;
Weeks passed before the part inscribed forgot 'em,
  The fleshy tablets, where the master's creed
Is written on boy's skin with birchen pen,
At each re-issue copied fair again.

This was the third edition, not the first,
  Printed on Arthur's bottom in red text
That very week, with comments interspersed,
  And cuts that left the student's eye perplexed,
Though in the love of flagellation versed,
  You hardly could tell one cut from the next;
All the smooth creamy paper, white and pink,
Was crossed and scored and blotted with red ink.

The fair full page of white and warm young flesh
  Was ruled across with long thick lines of red,
And lettered on the engraved backside with fresh
  Large characters, by all boys to be read,
In hieroglyphs fine as a spider's mesh,
  With copious coloured cuts illustrated,
Warm from the hand of the artist that begot 'em,
To adorn the bare blank page of Arthur's bottom.

All down the cream white margins, line on line,
   Ran the red tracery of the engraver's tool,
With many a capital and flourish fine,
   And ere the characters had time to cool
The well-soaked birch, still supple from the brine,
   Made a fresh score in sight of the whole school,
Who saw the inscription on the bare flesh scored,
While Arthur writhed with agony, and roared.

Like a large crimson flower of tropic lands
   That opens to the morning sun, and shuts
Again, at evening, and again expands,
   So Arthur's bottom seems, between the cuts,
To vibrate under his tormentor's hands,
   Who, gloating on it, as he flogs it, gluts
His eyes with the full prospect, while these great
Red cheeks contract at each cut, and dilate.

Then faster still the next few cuts are plied
   On those round naked fleshy hemispheres,
The rosy globes of Arthur's bare backside,
   The glowing cheeks that stream with crimson tears;
Cut after cut on Arthur's naked hide,
   And at each cut a fresh red streak appears,
And a fresh weal for each tough knotty bud,
And for each weal a fresh great flake of blood.

'By Jove! I say, he's getting peppered, ain't he?'
Thus Philip Shirley whispers Edward Beauchamp,
'And still the old one seems as fresh as paint, he
Swore he'd show all the school a sight to teach 'em
Next time; look there! the boy may well cry, mayn't he?
He thinks our bums were made for him to switch 'em,
Made to bear all the cuts he's pleased to allot 'em,
By Jove! just look at Clifford Minor's bottom!

All seamed with bloody weals and streaks vermilion,
That each cut makes blood run from in small streams,
He's got more cuts to show than Frank Tressilion,
And Frank's all scored behind with crimson seams.
I wouldn't have his bottom for a million,
There, the birch caught him nicely – how he screams!
Well, its a shame to try the poor lad farther.
I say, that stings, eh? How's your bottom, Arthur?'

He grins and whispers, but the boy scarce hears;
He struggles with the rising sobs, and chokes,
Striving in vain to swallow down his tears
And not cry out, since every cry provokes
Fresh punishment, and for each sob he fears
A fresh instalment of still sharper strokes;
And then the fresh cuts wring fresh tears and cries
From Arthur's quivering lips and streaming eyes.

His dark blue eyes look up, all dim with pain,
  From under his rough tangled yellow hair,
And plead for mercy piteously, in vain;
  The master never yet was known to spare;
Again his sinewy arm is raised, – again
  The rod comes whistling down on Arthur there,
And his bare haunches quiver from the blow.
'Oh! oh! oh! don't, please don't, sir! Oh! sir, oh!

Oh! let me off now, please, sir – please, sir, do, sir!
  I'll never – oh! – be late nor – oh! – miss church;
Oh; please, sir – Oh! sir, if you only knew, sir,'
  Cries Arthur, while the burning tears besmirch
His fair flushed cheeks, 'You'll cut my bottom
    through, sir,
  Oh! please, do stop, sir – do put down the birch –
Do, do, sir! please, sir! please, it cuts me so, sir!
I will take care, if you won't flog me – oh, sir!

I will, indeed I will, sir, try and mind –
  I won't, indeed I won't, be late again.'
But still the same birch lashed the boy behind,
  And the same cuts fell on him thick as rain,
And with arm raised and body half inclined
  To hit more hard and give more stinging pain
Through all the smarting bottom's breadth and length,
The master flogged the boy with all his strength.

As vigorously as his right hand could wield it,
    He plied the birch, till many a fragment broke
On the bare bottom with no shirt to shield it,
    The sensitive soft flesh without a cloak
All swollen and sore with crimson stripes that wealed it,
    All blood bespotted from the tingling stroke;
Till Arthur with clenched teeth began to suck
His rosy lips in, and get up his pluck.

Down came the birch; this time he did not squeak;
    Down came the birch; he hardly flinched from it;
Down came the birch; the blood rose to his cheek;
    Down came the birch; blood followed where it hit;
Down came the birch; he'll not sit down this week;
    Down came the birch; he didn't wince one bit;
Down came the birch; it cut him to the quick;
Down came the birch; he bore it like a brick.

He had cried at first as if he could not bear it,
    With eyes o'erflowing and imploring mien;
But as the strokes went on he plucked up spirit
    And smarting silently drew breath between,
As one who knows birch and won't seem to fear it,
    With all the cheek of schoolboys of thirteen;
As each cut fell he seemed to draw his bum tight
To bear the smart, with muscles braced up drum tight.

Though when he cried he had been well flogged
    for crying,
  He was flogged more now that he held his tongue;
He tried to hold out, and was flogged for trying;
  He was like some boys who seem always wrong,
Who are flogged for telling truth, and flogged for lying;
  It moved his master's bile that such a young
Boy should have cheek enough, even while he
    thrashed him,
Not to cry out beneath the twigs that lashed him.

This is the way with schoolmasters; their fashion
  Is to flog boys for silence as for speech;
If a boy blubbers while they lay the lash on
  They dry his tears with a fresh cut for each;
If he won't cry, it puts them in a passion,
  And they lay twice as much upon his breech;
So, if you cry, you're flogged; and if you don't,
You're flogged for impudence because you won't.

So was it with young Clifford; for his master
  First, for his first fault, flogged him till he cried,
And then because he cried, he flogged the faster,
  Till the weals grew as thick on his bare hide
As grains one shakes out of a pepper caster,
  Grains of red pepper on his red backside;
So that each cut drew down a fresh tear; but
  Each tear as surely drew down a fresh cut.

So Arthur stopped; but when he left off crying,
   The doctor flogged him harder than before
Because he sulked beneath the birch, defying
   The hand that flogged him, and the strokes he bore;
With all his might he laid each lash on, trying
   To increase the smart as he increased the score,
That each cut singly might give double pain,
And flogged the more because he flogged in vain.

For all the boys who saw him flogged would swear
   That Arthur took his flogging like a trump
After the first cuts; and it wasn't fair
   To lay so many on such a youngster's rump;
A pretty boy, too, with his white limbs bare,
   Round, rosy, naked haunches, fair and plump,
As ever served a school for laughing stock,
Was Arthur Clifford on the flogging block.

A pretty boy with fair flushed upturned face,
   Dark eyebrows and dark eyes, and yellow hair,
With breeches down for flogging, in disgrace;
   With the birch hanging over him in air,
With scar on scar and bloody trace on trace
   Of flogging all across the parts laid bare,
All his fair limbs and features drawn with pain,
As the birch showered its strokes on him like rain.

The bright tears on his long dark lashes hung,
    And on his soft cheeks stood like dew on peaches;
But though the birch twigs bit his flesh and stung,
    And at each following stroke drew blood like leeches.
No word of plaint now fell from Arthur's tongue,
    Though spots of red were on his shirt and breeches,
As the blood spun from his bare haunches, quivering
With pain that left his slender body shivering.

Till pausing, with an eye of sharp research,
    The master scanned the boy's round plump backside,
To see where best to apply the impending birch,
    Where to sting most, and mark the naked hide.
'Now, see, boys, what one gets for shirking church,'
    With eyes that glanced round all the school, he cried,
And raised the rod. 'You know now if you wish
For a good flogging, how to get it.' Swish!

Just where the broad bare bottom, smooth and plump,
    Flaked with red drops like rose leaf fallen on snow,
Sloped toward the tender thighs – there, worn to
      a stump,
    The frayed birch dealt its last and sharpest blow;
On either swelling cheek the whipped boy's rump
    Had fresh red lines and starting blood to show,
Even where the round cheeks gradually divide,
The specks of blood sprang bright on either side.

'That's all, for this time; now get up, boy.' As
   These words fell from the master's lips at last,
And Arthur heard, and rose, his bottom was
   A map of bloody lines, where lashes part
Had left the fair flesh one red quivering mass
   Of stripes and cuts and sores; so hard and fast
The birch had laid its strokes on, that his bottom
Not for a fortnight or a month forgot 'em.

He rose, and drew his trousers up, and turned
   Back to his place; tears on his face were yet,
And still his smarting bottom throbbed and burned,
   As he sat down with cheeks all flushed and wet,
And flinched, and then tried to seem unconcerned
   As far as pain would let him, when he met
The next boy's laughing eyes, and felt him jogging
His arm, 'Well, Arthur, how d'ye like your flogging?'

ETONENSIS

A Visit to Mrs Birch

A DRAMA

CHARACTERS

Mrs Birch

Miss Latecome

Miss Switchem

Miss Tickletouch

Sally

Young Ladies of the Academy

SCENE I

(School door - a passage)

SALLY *(sweeping)*   Dear me, what a thing it is to be at such a place as Mrs Birch's – hurry scurry – pell mell – always the mop and the brush in my hand, whilst mistress is using the birch broom with her dainty hands upon the round white bums of the little folks who come here to learn good manners.

MISS LATECOME *(within)*   Indeed, ma'am, I shall always come in good time if you will forgive me this once.

SALLY   She forgive you, indeed. I wish you may get it, young lady. She is more likely to give you double than to forgive half. But I must have a peep and see how things are going on. Where is my spying-hole? Oh, here it is. Now for a full view of the exhibition that is going on. Oh, there stands the mistress, with rod in hand, ready for the attack, and my little blubbering lady is lifting up her petticoats. There they are tucked up about her waist – and now she is loosening her drawers. I declare – down they go, sure enough. Now she is horsed! The mistress takes up her shift, and shows as pretty a bottom for a girl of fifteen as could well be seen. Now she begins to give it to her. One – two – Ah! she does not seem to like it She kicks and roars out famously over it. How red her bottom is already. What weals the rod leaves! Yet there is something very pleasant about it. I am delighted with it. Oh! dear, quite delightful. How charming it must be to give a pretty girl like this a good whipping. I should like it of all things in the world. To be sure I have sometimes a share in whipping the young ladies, but then it is only to horse them, or to hold them fast. I would much rather whip them myself. I would tickle their tobies soundly, I warrant – (*bell rings*) – Bless me, what can be wanted now. I suppose it is now some other unfortunate young lady's turn. Well – I must go and see.

SCENE II

(*Schoolroom*)

MRS BIRCH   Well, young ladies, our time of study is now up. School is over. You may now go and play.

OMNES   Thank you, ma'am, thank you.

MRS BIRCH   But be careful that you do not make too much noise, and as I am obliged to go out, I hope you will conduct yourselves remarkably well in my absence. Good morning, ladies.

(*Exit Mrs Birch*)

SUNDRY VOICES   Well, what shall we play at. 'Hunt the slipper' – No, 'Blind Nanny'. I don't like 'Blind Nanny'. I say let us play at 'Birds and Beasts'. Oh, no! that is a stupid game!

MISS LATECOME   I'll tell you what!

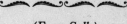

(Enter Sally)

SALLY   I think Miss Latecome had better play at 'Showing Her Marks'. She has a few – and pretty red ones they are, too. I saw them. How nicely she danced and sang over her bumbrushing this morning.

MISS LATECOME   I say, girls, here is a pretty go! She has been peeping; let us pay her off. What say you? You know mistress is out.

OMNES   With all our hearts.

MISS SWITCHEM   Catch hold of her girls, and down with her across the desk.

SALLY   Young ladies, what are you about? What is all this rudeness for? Why, you are pulling me across the desk, for shame. What are you going to do?

MISS SWITCHEM   Going to pay you off for peeping – that is all. We shall now see your marks – for marks you shall have – you shall have as sound a licked bottom as any of us ever had, for your 'Paul Pry' tricks.

SALLY   Why, surely ladies you don't mean – Oh, goodness, what are they about. They are taking up my clothes. I declare they have got them quite up. Sure as can be they mean to whip me. What shall I do? Oh, young ladies, for shame. Oh, dear, my bottom is completely naked before them all; and here comes the rod too. Oh, that I should have lived twenty-five years and have escaped the rod to get whipped at last by a parcel of girls. But, oh! mercy! the rod comes down; goodness, how it smarts. Oh, heavens! Oh, dear! Oh, pray, pray don't. Oh, oh, what shall I do? Oh, ladies, do forgive me. I shall never peep again. Oh, dear, I can't bear it any more, indeed I can't. It hurts me so dreadfully, it does indeed. Oh! pray, pray don't. Oh! mercy, mercy. Oh, my bottom; what will become of me, ladies? Oh, ladies, for mercy's sake release me – there, thank you. I won't peep again, ladies.

MISS LATECOME   Now, Mrs Sally, we have seen your marks, and I venture to say that your bottom is wealed to the full as well as mine.

MISS SWITCHEM   Quite as well. But mind, Mrs Sally, not one word to the Mistress, take notice, or you shall have a worse flogging than this.

SALLY   Oh, I am dumb, you may depend upon me. I shall not want to exhibit my naked bottom before a schoolroom of young ladies any more.

OMNES   Ha, ha, ha.

MISS SWITCHEM   Well, Miss Latecome, you peppered her in good style. She will not soon forget the way you laid it into her. Come now, let us go out to the playground.

OMNES   Come along.

SCENE III

Schoolroom. Scholars in one part of the room and
Mrs Birch and Miss Tickletouch by themselves in another.

MRS BIRCH   My dear Miss Tickletouch, you have longed to see a whipping, here is now an excellent opportunity. Miss Drawler, although so very beautiful a girl, knows not a word of her lesson. She must be whipped as an example to the others, for were I to excuse her there would be no getting a lesson from any of them.

MISS TICKLETOUCH   Indeed, my dear Mrs Birch, I think nothing can justify her idleness; and as she can do better if she likes, this only calls the more loudly for punishment.

MRS BIRCH   That is exactly my opinion, so ring at once for Sally. As she has never yet been whipped, I suppose we shall have a fine crying bout of it.

MISS TICKLETOUCH (*rings*)   You must not mind that, but go through with it with becoming spirit.

(*Enter Sally*)

MRS BIRCH   Sally reach me down the rod. Miss Drawler come out. Your neglect of your lessons must be punished with a good whipping.

MISS DRAWLER   A good whipping, ma'am, why I never was whipped in my life.

34

MRS BIRCH   That makes no difference to me; as long as you come to my school you must submit to the treatment of a scholar; and that you know is to be whipped for neglect of lessons; so come forward, Miss, and lie down upon the sofa.

MISS DRAWLER   No, indeed, ma'am, I shall not. I never was whipped yet; and at my age I am determined I never shall be.

MRS BIRCH   Very well, miss, we shall soon see as to that. But remember, this resistance will only cost you double.

MISS DRAWLER   It shall cost me nothing, for I am determined I won't submit. Leave me alone. Where are you dragging me? Let me go, Sally, let me go.

MRS BIRCH   Now, Sally, down with her across the sofa; that is right. She is now safe. Hold her hands down, I shall throw up her clothes; there they are. A little higher will be better. That will do, her bottom is quite uncovered now. There, Sally, keep her clothes up so, while I tickle her soundly.

MISS TICKLETOUCH   (*gazes intently on the scene*)

MISS DRAWLER   What are you doing? Leave my clothes alone. You shan't take them up. Oh, dear, what shall I do? I never was whipped in my life, and I can't bear it. Oh! oh! good gracious. Oh, don't hurt me so. Oh, how dreadfully it stings. Oh, my bottom, my poor bottom. I can't bear it; I can't, indeed I can't. Pray, pray let me go. I shall be such a good girl in future. Oh! for heaven's sake let me go I can't bear any more, indeed I can't; it will drive me mad. Oh, dear, oh, dear. Oh, this is dreadful. Oh! oh!

MRS BIRCH   There, miss, you see who has conquered at last, eh? Well you have now been whipped in spite of your earnest declarations to the contrary. And I hope it will be of lasting service to you. You may now retire to your seat, miss, and I hope the next whipping you get you will not be quite so impertinent about it. (*Miss Drawler sits down*)

To Miss Tickletouch

Well, my dear Miss Tickletouch, you do seem to enjoy the spectacle of a good whipping.

MISS TICKLETOUCH   I think it the most delightful treat I ever witnessed. The young lady's personal beauty added so much to the interest of the scene. What a beautiful form she has, and what complexion! Her bottom is full large, and fair as alabaster itself, or at least was so before the smart application of your rod, which speedily altered its hue; so that, surrounded by the other parts glittering in their unsullied whiteness, it resembled a rose in a bed of lilies.

MRS BIRCH   You speak, my dear Miss Tickletouch, in glowing terms. You must have found it a very interesting scene.

MISS TICKLETOUCH   So much so, my dear Mrs Birch, that I own I felt a great desire to become a partaker in a similar one, though not in quite so public a manner. It is so many years since I felt the rod that I have but a faint recollection of its taste. This interesting scene has raised in me a strong desire to revive it.

MRS BIRCH   I understand you. There is a great pleasure in recalling to remembrance the events of our childhood, and you would like to have done to you something similar to what your governess formerly did.

MISS TICKLETOUCH   You have exactly hit it. I should indeed like to prove once more the effects of the Birchen Discipline.

MRS BIRCH   Well, my dear, after the young ladies are in bed this evening I shall just tickle your lovely bottom a little, though I suppose you would not like it quite so severely as Miss Drawler had it.

MISS TICKLETOUCH   Not quite, if you please; however do it sufficiently to make me feel it, and as a punishment too, or all the effect would be destroyed.

MRS BIRCH   Bless me, what is all that disturbance in the playground? Is Bedlam broke loose? What can it mean? Run Louisa, my dear, to the window and see.

MISS LOUISA BIRCH   Mamma, it is Miss Switchem who is pulling the hair of a little girl who is crying.

MRS BIRCH   Indeed, then desire Miss Switchem to come up here instantly. I shall teach her better behaviour. I shall see what the rod will do for her.

(Exit Miss Birch)

37

MISS TICKLETOUCH   Why, surely, my dear madam, you do not mean to whip a great girl of eighteen?

MRS BIRCH   Indeed I do – and you shall see it too. If I did not take some authority upon me these overgrown girls would trample upon me. Yes, yes. I shall whip her, and do it well too.

(*Enter Miss Birch and Miss Switchem*)

MRS BIRCH   Come here, miss. How dare you behave in this extraordinary manner, and torment a little girl so much younger than yourself? Ring the bell, my dear.

(*Miss Birch rings*)

MISS SWITCHEM   She was very saucy to me, ma'am.

MRS BIRCH   That is no excuse for your behaving so to her, and for this I shall certainly punish you. (*Enter Sally*) Sally, you are just come in time to assist in whipping this girl, this forward young lady. Come, miss, take up your petticoats. What! you don't seem inclined, eh? Oh, very well. I dare say we shall be able to manage you amongst us. Sally, hold up her hands; there, that will do. Now I have her petticoats up, and I shall have her drawers down in a trice – there they are about her heels. Now, Sally, horse her as they do in the boys' school. Give me the rod, Miss Tickletouch – pray take your part in this affair, and hold up her chemise while I warm her bottom. There, miss, I hope that will teach you to behave better to the little girls in future.

Miss Switchem   Oh! oh! oh! pray, ma'am, pray don't – I shall never do so any more. I never will, indeed I won't. Oh! heavens! Oh! heavens! what shall I do? Oh! pray don't strike so hard. Oh, dear! oh, dear! Oh! oh! oh!

Mrs Birch   There, you may let her down now, Sally. And you, miss, put your clothes in order, and go to the playground, and see that you are more careful of your conduct in future.

(Exit Sally and Miss Switchem)

Miss Tickletouch   Really, my dear Mrs Birch, you are an excellent manager, and I think you use a rod charmingly. What do you think, my dear Miss Birch?

Mrs Birch   I know perfectly well how Mamma uses it. I can speak from experience.

Miss Tickletouch   Indeed – do you then ever taste it?

Mrs Birch   Frequently. Indeed I would not swear that my bottom is now free from the marks, for it is but four days since I was soundly tickled for neglecting my music lesson.

Miss Tickletouch   But you know it is purely for your benefit.

Miss Birch   It is hard to think so while the lash is descending, for it then stings so dreadfully, but no sooner does the lashing cease than the pain ceases also.

MRS BIRCH   My dear Louisa, see the young ladies to bed and retire yourself.

(Exit Miss Birch)

Now, my dear Miss Tickletouch, the scholars have all retired. This is your time to make the desired experiment, but are you sure you have fortitude enough to go through with it.

MISS TICKLETOUCH   To ensure that, we shall call on Sally's assistance. She shall hold me as she did Miss Drawler, and I beg that should I exclaim ever so much, she will make me go on until I have received at least two dozen.

MRS BIRCH   It shall be as you wish. Sally – *(Enter Sally)* – Miss Tickletouch has an inclination to try the effect of a whipping, so she requests you will hold her as you did Miss Drawler, while she receives a sound tickling.

SALLY   Certainly, ma'am. Come, miss, lay yourself down on your face across the sofa – so – that is right.

MRS BIRCH   Now, Sally, take up Miss Tickletouch's clothes high enough to leave her bottom completely naked. Why, my dear Miss Tickletouch, you have so charming a bottom that I think it is almost a pity to raise a weal upon it.

SALLY   I think so, too. Her bottom – although she is two-and-thirty – is as round and as plump as Miss Drawler's at eighteen.

MISS TICKLETOUCH   Pray proceed while my courage is good; and don't let my bottom be spared on account of its complexion.

MRS BIRCH   Well, my dear Miss T., here goes. One – two – three – and –

MISS TICKLETOUCH   Oh! oh! oh! dear Mrs Birch – pray – you hurt me – you do, indeed. Sally, let me go – let me go. Oh! dear, oh! oh! oh!

MRS BIRCH   Well, my fair unfortunate pupil – how do you like to be whipped?

MISS TICKLETOUCH   Why, to tell you the truth it seems during the operation almost too much to bear – but immediately after, it leaves a delightful glow which more than repays the momentary inconvenience.

MRS BIRCH   I think you are right, and, if you wish it, you shall have another taste or two of it before you depart. Supper is now on the table. The Doctor has returned and wants your company. Come, my dear, we will join him.

(Exeunt)

*Hints on Flogging, showing how to Enjoy it
to Perfection, in a Letter to a Lady*

MADAM – I hear that you have just opened a birching
establishment in Pimlico. I wish you every success, and
believe you will attain it. Your personal qualifications for *une
fouetteuse* are excellent. You are just about the right age, for
you cannot be more than thirty. Your figure, as it should,
inclines decidedly to plumpness, and your arms are strong,
and finely rounded. With the right sleeve turned up, the
movement of the biceps muscle when you are birching,
must be most fetching to beholders, especially if a good view
can also be obtained of the round full breasts while they are
heaving with the exertion. Your countenance too is full of
animation, and no one can have ever seen you in a rage and
marked your flushing cheeks, clenched teeth and gleaming
eyes, without longing for a birching at your fair hands. Your
qualifications for the post you are about to undertake being
so unquestionable, it may seem somewhat impertinent on
my part to offer you any suggestions upon the conduct of
your business. But, as a considerable experience of the
society of whipping ladies has enabled me to see that very
few of the establishments in question, chiefly through

42

ignorance on the part of the proprietresses of the real wants of their patrons, meet the requirements of the day, I venture to lay before you, firstly, wherein, in my opinion, the true secret lies of winning gentlemen's hearts by whipping their bottoms; and secondly, how to attain that end.

Birching is a sensuous as much as a sensual pleasure. The mere application of a bunch of twigs to the posteriors by the aid of a mechanical apparatus would produce the same physical effect, as far as the surface of the posteriors was concerned, as a rod wielded by a woman, but it would not cause the same sensuous gratification. This shows that to give your patrons the true enjoyment of the game all the incidental accessories to the act must be carefully attended to. One of the great charms of birching lies in the sentiment that the floggee is the powerless victim of the furious rage of a beautiful woman. Therefore, to secure the perfect realisation of the idea, there should be simulated on the part of the flogger, passionate anger with her subject, and on the part of the floggee or patient, powerlessness to resist the punishment inflicted, fear of the operation and a desire to escape the punishment.

Now, when a gentleman calls upon one of these birching ladies, and is asked how many dozen he will take, and she administers the strokes with an agreeable smile on her face, and stops short the moment that he says, 'That will do, thank you,' the illusion is wholly ignored, which it is necessary to keep up fully to appreciate the enjoyment of being birched; and the gentleman buttons up his trousers and goes away, thinking that the pleasures of the rod are vastly overrated, and the sport of birching a very poor one after all.

Now to remedy this evil, and to put birching in its proper light before all the frequenters of your establishment, I propose that you should keep a small book containing a series of birch scenes, written in a dramatic form, which, when your visitor calls, you should put into his hands, and ask him which of them he would like to enact with you. His part would be got up in a moment, and you, of course, would be up in the ladies' parts in all of them; strict adherence to the exact words of the text would not be necessary, the scenes merely being intended as plans or outlines of the relations in which you would pretend to stand towards one another during the operation, the style of conversation you should use, and the performance you should go through. Previous to commencing the drama it should, of course, be arranged what number of strokes your visitor should receive, and that being settled it should be understood that no solicitations or prayers or entreaties for mercy or struggles on his part, which, of course, to keep up the illusion he will make, should influence you to reduce the number agreed on. For the sake of example, I will suppose a gentleman, whom we will name Mr Jones, has called. After mutual salutations, he tells you that his number is three dozen, and if he does not know your system you tell him that whatever number he fixes on he will have to receive whether he likes it or not, as compulsory flogging is your theory of the pleasure of birching. Upon his agreeing to this, you produce your book, each drama or scene in which has its separate heading, and ask him to choose the one he would like to act with you, pointing out to him that the stage directions as to slaps, boxes on the ear, hair pulling, etc., will be rigidly carried out unless he says beforehand that he wishes them omitted. Upon an understanding being come to, I will suppose he selects one of the pieces for your joint performance, of which the following sketch will serve as an example. I will call it:

The Enraged and Jealous Wife

SHE (*rushing up to the gentleman, and giving him several boxes on the ear, which he vainly tries to save himself from*) You beast, you brute, how dare you look me in the face after what I saw with my own eyes?

HE My dear, if you will only let me explain.

SHE (*interrupting him with another resounding slap on the cheek*) Explain! explain, indeed! I should like to know how you could explain – did I not catch you in the privy with Mary, with one arm round her waist and one somewhere else, and your own breeches in a state of disorder – (*another slap*) – and did I not I listen at the door, which you had forgot to fasten first, and hear you say you were so pleased to find she did not wear drawers, and do you think because I've discharged her I've done with the matter? No, sir, I've a rod for you, and an arm that can use it, too, and I'll exercise it till I draw blood – see if I don't.

Off with your trousers this minute – (*he pulls them off trembling*) – your boots and drawers, too, for I'll have nothing to keep your arse from my rod – (*he pulls off his boots and drawers*) – yes, and your shirt, for I wouldn't be bothered to pin up the tail of it – (*he pulls off his shirt, having nothing on but his flannel waistcoat and socks*). Ah, my fine fellow, now we'll settle our accounts. Lie down on the bed immediately (*he does so, and she takes a rod from the drawer*). There, there, there, you beast! – (*whipping him with all her might*) – there; I'll make this white bottom as red as a rose. I'll make it blush if its owner can't!

HE   Oh! oh! I can't stand it; pray have mercy (*gets up and runs round the table*).

SHE (*running after and whipping him all the time*)   Oh! you think you can get away, do you? I've locked the door, and can run as fast as you.

HE (*turning round and pretending to try to get the rod from her*)   I can't stand it, I tell you, put down the rod.

SHE   Put down the rod, indeed! thank you, sir, for your advice. Your bottom has got a good deal more beating to stand, I can tell you; I've not half warmed it (*she pushes him away, so that he falls on his face on the bed, and continues the flogging*).

HE   Oh: for God's sake forgive me; you're so awfully strong, you might show some mercy (*runs away again, she after him, flogging all the time*).

SHE   Run away, sir. I like the fun. Get up – get up, you lazy brute (*following and birching him. Having completed the whipping, she throws aside the rod and, approaching him with an air of arrogance and haughtiness as he leans panting against a chair, tells him to fall down and beg forgiveness, which he does in a very meek and penitent manner. After which he resumes his clothing.*)

Besides dramas of this kind, which of course could be multiplied to any number, I think you would find it very advantageous always to have in your mind a few stories relating to birching with which you might amuse your visitors before commencing operations, or which you might share during dinner with one of your admirers. I cannot imagine anything more delightful than a dinner with you in a private room at the Solferino or Royal, or at your own house, during which we should tell each other tales of birching – real or invented. I think I see our heightening colour and glistening eyes and restless motions on our chairs as the champagne circulates, and the salacious thoughts kindled by the luscious strokes of whipping burn in our excited brains.

As the soup was served, and when the waiter had left the room (if it was a female servant we should not mind conversing before her), perhaps I should begin with some such anecdote as the following:

'My dear, I've just had such an unexpected treat. Walking in the park I noticed a nursery-maid in conversation with a soldier by the Serpentine. Her charge – a boy of about nine – had wandered away from her, and was walking along the brink of the water. The conversation with her companion was too absorbing to allow her to look after the boy, who was pleased enough to take advantage of her being otherwise occupied, and was amusing himself with sailing such little bits of stick as he could pick up. Suddenly a cry from him informed her that while stooping forward to sail one of his extemporised vessels he had overbalanced himself, and fallen forward on his hands and knees into the shallow water.

'Beyond getting wet he was in no danger, and to catch him up was the work of a moment for the girl. "Oh, you naughty boy," cried she, red as fire with vexation and rage, "won't I make your arse tingle for this!" At these words I approached her and said, "I think you are right; such dangerous tricks should be put a stop to at once by a good whipping." She, pleased to find that I agreed with her in laying the fault on the child, curtsied, and said, "Yes, sir, and that he shall have, I'll warrant, before another minute." And in a twinkling she had his breeches down, and putting her left arm round his head and shoulders, inflicted a shower of heavy slaps with her right hand till she was out of breath with the exertion. The child bellowed and kicked lustily, and I was afraid lest his screams should cause some of the passers-by to interfere, but nobody seemed to think the matter any business of theirs, and I had the pleasure of enjoying the sight of as sound a whipping as I could wish to see. The minx had an arm like a sledge-hammer, and when she had done, the boy's bottom was as red as her face, which was the colour of beetroot. "There you little beast," she cried, setting him free at last, "if ever you get into the like mischief again I'll flay you alive."

'The effect of this scene upon me you may imagine, and I was unable to move from where I was standing for some time afterwards. Approaching the girl, I gave her half-a-crown, telling her to accept it as a token of my regard for the excellent discipline with which she managed children. "I should think," said I, "your mistress must highly value you as a nurse-maid." "Lord bless you, sir, missus would send me away at a minute's notice if she knowed as I flogged one of 'em." "Then are you not afraid of his telling his mamma?" asked I. "He dare not, or else he would fast enough," answered she with a grim smile; "the first time I whipped him he stamped and said he would tell his mamma when she came home. 'Will you?' said I, having him across my knee in a jiffey, 'will you, will you, will you? – not until I've flayed your arse for you, though,' and I kept on spanking it, sir, for a good quarter of an hour in spite of his promises not to tell." "But I should have thought," interrupted I, "he would have told all the same when his mother returned." "Not he, sir, for I didn't let the matter rest there, but told him if ever he said a word to his mamma about the whippings I gave him, Mr Jones, my young man as he was then, would come as soon as he went to sleep, and carry him off to a place where they whipped little boys with red hot wire, and as my young man was in the kitchen at the time, I called him up to speak to the truth of what I said, which he did. So you see, sir, I've that child's bottom as much at my disposal as if it was my own, and its only by spanking of their behinds as you can do anything with children."

'Wasn't this a charming morning's amusement, dear?'

Then after laughing over my story, and congratulating me on the treat I have had, you would probably begin as follows:

'Ah, that is the sort of girl though that I would not have for a nursery-maid myself if I had children. I should look upon their bottoms as my preserve, and wouldn't allow any poachers. I should always tell a servant that if she had any complaint against a child of mine she must let me know, and then if he deserved it, I'd give his arse such a warming as ought to satisfy any reasonable woman.

'But your story reminds me of a birching I had the pleasure of giving my little sister the other day. I think I mentioned to you that I have a little sister of about fourteen living with me. Well, she only came to stay with me about a week ago, and I assure you she hadn't been in the house a couple of hours, so plump and chubby was she, but I burned for an excuse for using one of my rods on that round bottom of hers. She is such a very good steady girl that I could find no excuse for birching her, so I determined to create one. Giving her the keys of my sideboard one day, I told her that I was going out of town for a day or two, and that I wished her to take charge of them while I was away, reminding her that she was to touch nothing there till I came back. As she knew that there was cake, wine and preserves there, I felt quite sure I should not be obeyed. Putting on my bonnet, and taking a handbag with me to give an air of probability to my story, I sent Sarah for a cab. I gave the direction loud enough for Lucy, my sister, to hear, "Waterloo Station," cried I, and drove off.

'When I had driven a little way I stopped the cab, got out, and after making a few purchases, walked towards home, feeling sure that my little puss couldn't refrain for long from the contents of the sideboard. What glowing pictures I conjured up, as I walked along, of her plump arse wriggling under my swishes. My heart beat with excitement as I quietly let myself in by a latch-key and crept softly upstairs to the dining-room. Peeping through the keyhole, I could scarcely repress a shriek of delight, for my plan had succeeded, and I saw Lucy seated on the floor before the open sideboard with a plate of almonds and raisins in her lap. I burst into the room with an – "Oh, you naughty girl – after what I told you – but I know how to punish you, miss." And I flew to the bell and rang it. "Bring me a rod, Sarah" said I, when my servant appeared. And then turning to my young lady, "Now, miss," said I, "what have you to say in excuse?" Of course she coloured and began to blub, and said she was very sorry, but she had not taken more than two raisins. "If you had only taken half a one it would have been just the same – for disobedience is what I will stand from no little girl," answered I. Then Sarah appeared with the rod, at which Miss set up a shout, and begged me not to whip her, as she never had been whipped at school even. "Then they must have grossly neglected their duty to you," said I, "if such was the case, and that makes it all the more necessary for me to supply the omission," and, calling Sarah to help, I soon had her nicely across my knee, and turned up her clothes while Sarah pulled down her drawers, and you may imagine, dear, what followed. I didn't spare her bottom, I assure you, nor mind her bellowings, but whipped her backside till my arm ached – and not before I drew blood, I may add. The little minx could hardly sit down the next day, so stiff and sore was she from the whipping I gave her.'

These and suchlike anecdotes might conduce to the enjoyment of a *tête-à-tête* dinner or supper party very greatly.

Apologising, dear madame, for detaining you over this very long letter, believe me, your obedient servant,

ALLAN BUMMINGHAM

❧❦❧

Reginald's Flogging

PART I

Reggie Fane sat at his father's foot
   Sighing and making a mane,
And out and spake his auld father,
   'What ails ye Reggie Fane, my boy? What
      ails ye, Reggie Fane?'

'I ail and I quail, dear father,' he says,
   'And I can tell you why;
There's a good birch rod for my bottom
   Would make a tall boy cry, father, would
      make a tall boy cry!'

' 'Gin the birch be cut for your bottom
   I wish ye may be well swished,
I wish ye a good stout rod, my boy,
   The best that ever was wished, Reggie, and
      the best that ever was wished.

' 'Gin your master take your breeches down
    I wish he may switch you well,
Well may he breech you, hard may he switch
        you,
    Till your bottom burn and swell, Reggie, till
        your bottom burn and swell!'

'Bare will he strip me, hard will he whip me,
    I wot on a bare broad part,
The buds are rough, and the twigs are tough,
    And oh! but I shall smart, father; oh, but I
        shall smart!

'The twigs are long and the switches are strong,
    The shoots are straight and lithe;
First a stripping and then a whipping,
    And oh! this bottom will writhe, father, and
        oh, this bottom will writhe.'

'The man that whips your bottom, my boy,
    Oh, blessed may that man be,
My his arm be strong, may his reach be long,
    May he give you three dozen and three,
        Reggie, three dozen good cuts and three.

'The rod that's bound for your bottom
    A good tight rod may it be,

May you get the best whipping that ever boy got,
　　And may all your schoolfellows see, Reggie,
　　　　may all your schoolfellows see.'

Now Reggie Fane stands at the schoolhouse door,
　　Crying and making a mane,
And by there came his brother Fred,
　　'What ails ye, Reggie Fane, brother? What
　　　　ails ye Reggie Fane?'

'I ache and I quake, dear brother,' he says,
　　'And I can tell you why;
There's to be such a jolly good swishing the morn,
　　And who's to be swished but I, Freddy?
　　　　who's to be swished but I?'

'If you're to be swished again, brother,
　　I'm sure it serves you right;
May the birch lay on hard to your bare bottom,
　　May it lay the cuts on tight, Reggie, may it
　　　　lay the cuts on tight.

'You'll wear out all the birch in the countryside,
　　As sure as my name's Fred;
You were swished on Sunday, swished on Monday,
　　And swished all roaring and red, Reggie,
　　　　swished all roaring and red.'

54

Now Reggie Fane in the school cloister,
    Writhing with fore felt pain.
And by came all the schoolfellows,
    'What ails ye, Reggie Fane, you dunce?
        What ails ye, Reggie Fane?'

'I shake and I quake, my mates,' he says,
    'And I can show you why,
The rod and my bottom are not betrothed,
    The red birch rod and I, my boys, the red
        birch rod and I.'

'We were hoping and wishing to see a good
        swishing
    That leaves the birch twigs red;
There were twelve boys flogged yesterday,
    And all were switched till they bled, Reggie,
        and they all were switched till they bled.

'The first was Philip, the second was Charles,
    The next were Walter and Fred.
Charlie was swished till he roared with the pain,
    And Philip was switched till he bled, Reggie,
        Philip was switched till he bled.

'Edward was swished till the blood ran down,
    And oh! boys, didn't he roar.
And the rod was laid on Hugh's bottom,

Till the master could flog no more, Reggie,
   till he could flog no more.

'You should have seen his tail, Reggie,
   The reddest of schoolboy tails,
It was just a map of ridges and cuts,
   Of cuts and weals and wales, Reggie, of
      bloody weals and wales.

'Ernest was flogged till he bled and cried,
   Mingling salt flood with flood,
And Alfred's bottom had cut after cut,
   Till the red rod ran with blood, Reggie, and
      the bare bum blushed with blood.

'You could not count on Tom's bottom
   A tithe of the cuts he had;
He was flogged till the rafters rang with his
      roars,
   With the roars of a tortured lad, Reggie, the
      screams of a bleeding lad.

'There were more weals on Arthur's bottom
   Than stars in the sky at night;
His bottom was red 'ere his flogging was done,
   That was so soft and white, Reggie, so soft a
      bum and white.

'Herbert was flogged till the birchen twigs
   Broke off in the cuts they made:
Till the twigs broke short on his bare bottom,
   And left his bottom flayed, Reggie, his
      smarting bottom flayed.

'The twigs that were laid on Frank's bottom,
   His very blood they drank;
At the thirtieth stroke they bent and they broke,
   They broke on the bottom of Frank, Reggie,
      the well-flogged bottom of Frank.

'And Willie was swished the morn, Reggie,
   And Willie's bottom is red.
And Rob was switched till he roared again,
   And Harry was switched till he bled, Reggie,
      Harry was switched till he bled.

'Edmund was horsed on Algernon's back,
   And there he rode bare breeched;
And Algernon's bottom was lashed on the
      block,
   And they were both jolly well switched,
      Reggie, and they were jolly well switched.

'Edmund's bottom is red as a rose,
   The cuts on it fresh as he got 'em;

Algernon's bottom is red as a peach,
  It's redder than Edmund's bottom, Reggie,
    redder than Edmund's bottom.

'And Leonard got such a swishing,
  He bled at each cut as he got 'em;
There's never a flower and never a fruit
  As red as Leonard's bottom, Reggie, as
    Leonard's great red bottom.

'And won't you catch it, Reggie, my boy,
  Won't you flinch when your turn comes;
The birch will brush your bum across
  Till it matches their well-whipped bums,
    Reggie, till it's colour out-blushes their
    bums.

'Frank will look whole and sound to you
  And Willie and Fred white breeched;
Edmund's bum will be nothing to your's,
  For oh! but you'll get well switched, Reggie,
    your bottom will get well switched.'

PART II

Now Reggie Fane stands at his master's desk,
    Watching his master's frown,
And out then spake his auld master,
    'Now take your breeches down, Reggie, now
        take your breeches down.'

Oh, curly and fair was his thick soft hair,
    And bright his bonny blue 'ee,
But the marks that were on his bottom
    Were a piteous sight to see, my boys, were a
        piteous sight to see.

'Now give me here my good birch rod,
    That is both stout and tough,
And take up his shirt now, two of you boys,
    And you shall have cuts enough, Reggie, your
        bum shall have cuts enough.'

They set him on the flogging block,
    They set him on his knee;
And the flush on his face and the flush on his
        bum
    Was a stunning sight to see, my boys, was a
        stunning sight to see.

Charlie and Fred stood at Reginald's head,
   And Algernon stood at his feet;
And Hugh stood by, and Willie was nigh,
   And Arthur and Frank as was meet, my boys,
      to take their turn as was meet.

Up then stood that proud master,
   His birch in hand he's ta'en,
He's laid it well into Reggie's bottom,
   'Take that to begin with, Fane,' he says, 'take
      that to begin with, Fane.'

Never a word spoke Reginald then,
   But he winced and flushed with pain;
The next good cut on Reginald's bottom,
   'And how do you like it, Fane?' he says, 'does
      it sting? does it sting you, Fane?'

Oh, fain was Reggie to rub his bottom,
   To rub it with his shirt;
As he laid the rod on Reginald's bottom,
   'Does it hurt, my boy, does it hurt?' he says,
      'Eh, Reggie, my boy, does it hurt?'

The first six cuts on Reggie's bottom
   He hardly winced at all;
But at every cut on Reggie's bottom
   You could see the salt tears fall, my boys, the
      thick tears gather and fall.

But wae's my heart for Reggie's bottom,
  When the seventh and eighth cuts fell,
The red blood ran from Reggie's bottom,
  For Reggie was flogged right well, my boys,
    for his bottom was flogged right well.

The next three cuts on Reggie's bottom,
  They made it very sore,
But at the twelfth it was bloody and wealed,
  And he could not choose but roar, poor boy,
    he could not choose but roar.

The next few cuts on Reggie's bottom,
  It reddened more and more,
As the red rod fell on his tender flesh,
  On the weals that it made before, poor boy,
    on the weals that it raised before.

'Oh, look at his bottom, Algernon!
  Oh, isn't it jolly and red!
Oh, Reggie, I wouldn't be you, my boy;
  Oh, look at the weals there, Fred, by Jove!
    the stripes, and the blood, then, Fred.

'Oh, look at his weals, and guess what he feels,
  Oh, isn't his bottom sore!
Oh, look at the cuts in his flesh, what nuts!
  Oh, doesn't the pain make him roar, by Jove!
    Oh, doesn't he cry and roar.

'Oh, hold his shirt up, Algernon,
  Hold the boy's shirt up high;
Let us all have a view of his bottom, Hugh,
  Oh, doesn't the pain make him cry, by Jove!
    Oh, doesn't the pain make him cry.

'Oh, isn't it nuts to see so many cuts,
  And think it's young Reggie who's got 'em!
It won't be done this hour, what fun!
  Oh, look at his jolly red bottom, by Jove! Oh,
    I say, what a stunning red bottom!

'Oh, isn't it ruddy, and ridgy and bloody!
  Oh, don't I know what he feels!
How he yells with the pain; well, I wouldn't be
    Fane,
  Oh, isn't it covered with weals, I say! and
    ain't they jolly big weals!

'Look, by Jove, though he's trying, he is, to stop
    crying,
  You'll catch it, by Jove, Reggie Fane!
Ah, my boy, it won't do – well. I wouldn't be
    you!
  How his bottom goes in with the pain, by Jove!
    how it winces and shrinks with the pain.

'Oh, haven't I wished to see Reginald swished,
　　And count up the cuts as he got 'em?
But, by Jove, you can't count such an awful
　　　　amount,
　　You can only look at his bottom, by Jove! at
　　　　the weals that are on his bottom.

'There are six – what nuts! no, seven more cuts –
　　Nine cuts in a breath, by God!
Oh, look at him, do! is he blubbering, Hugh?
　　Oh, they're bringing another good rod, by
　　　　Jove! a jolly good stinging new rod.

'There, there now, swish! as a fellow could wish!
　　Well this is a swishing to see!
You remember I said to the boy's brother Fred,
　　What a sight for a school it would be, my boys,
　　　　what a stunning good sight it would be!

'There, swish! swish! swish! Well, I almost
　　　　could wish . . .
　　By Jove, though isn't it nuts?
Well, I give you joy of it, Reggie, my boy!
　　Ah, there were two sharp fleshy cuts, by Jove!
　　　　two right down stinging good cuts.

'Oh, Algernon – do let me see there, Hugh!
　　I want a good sight of his bottom;

Have you got a good view of the cuts on it, too?
    And to think it's young Reggie who's got 'em,
        by Jove, that curly-haired youngster who's
        got 'em.

'Who's as sorry and fair if you look at him there,
    Well, this really is more than I wished!
Aye, well may he roar! Yes, it really is more,
    But isn't he getting well swished! my eyes;
        Ah, isn't he getting well swished!

' "Bring a rod!" What, a third? Come, I say, on
        my word,
    Its a chouse – its a thundering shame!
' "Bring a rod there!" I wish – there – swish!
        swish! swish!
    I say though, ain't it a game, my boys? I say,
        Frank, ain't it a game?

'Oh, many's the bum I've seen swished since
        I've come,
    And many's the swishing I've had,
But I never saw yet, and I ne'er shall forget
    Such a swishing as that of this lad, I trow, this
        yellow-haired, rosy-cheeked lad.

'Stand aside again, Hugh, and let's look at him,
      do!
  Do, Algernon, let me see!
The weals and cuts are like ridges and ruts,
   Oh, ain't his bottom a spree, Willie, his
      bloody wealed bottom a spree?

'Left cheek and right, it is all the same sight,
  It's all one blossom of red,
Of red wetted flesh, with the cuts in it fresh,
   And the sores where his bottom has bled, Will,
      where his poor little bottom has bled.

'Oh, by Jove! how he squeaks! and his broad
      hinder cheeks
  How they quiver afresh at each blow!
If he's rosy above as a little boy love,
   I'll swear he's rosier below, my boys, the
      rod's made him rosier below.

'See the master there, Will, how he's flogging
      him still,
  At each cut how he does lay the lash on,
I can tell you, young Fane, you may roar out
      with pain,
   But you won't move the master's compassion,
     my boy, though you may move your
     comrades' compassion.

'There! hush! did you hear him? I say, boys
near him,
Is his bottom cut right to the bone?
Has his birch cut him through? has it cut him in
two?
Why can't he let him alone, I trow, let the
poor naked bottom alone?

'It's worth while though to see what a flogging
can be –
Reggie Fane knows by this time, I'll swear!
And its written, I think, pretty broad in red ink,
On his bottom so broad and so bare, my
boys, on his red flesh naked and bare.

'Swish! swish! what, another? he looks at his
brother,
And Freddy begins to cry;
He begins to blub, too – Fred, if I were you,
I'd rather my brother than I, by Jove! I'd
rather he smarted than I.

'Oh, hark, you fellows, by Jove, how he bellows!
Oh, hark to Reginald, hark!
"Oh, sir, I can't bear it. Oh, spare me, do spare."
Oh, ain't Reggie's flogging a lark, my boys,
and ain't Reggie Fane a good lark?

'What again and again! Well done, Reggie Fane!
  Swish! oh, swish! Hark to him! Oh!
Now, Reggie! now, Rod! Its a chorus, by God –
  And each cut makes the red drops flow, my
      boys, and Reginald roars as they flow.

'There, it's over at last, never mind, man, it's past;
  It isn't, by Jupiter, no!
It's a chouse then – I wish he was Reggie
      there – swish!
    There, didn't he just sing out, oh, my boys?
      ah, didn't the boy sing out, oh?'

Reggie Fane get up sobbing, with all his stripes
      throbbing,
  He roars as he rises, hark,
With the tears in his eyes, from the block see
      him rise –
    'Oh, ain't a good flogging a lark, my boys,
      and ain't Reggie Fane a good lark?'

Now Reggie Fane stands in his schoolfellows' midst,
  Crying and roaring with pain;
And out then spake his schoolmaster,
  'Let me hear no more noise there, Fane,' he
      says, 'stop crying this instant, Fane.

'Stop crying, you dunce, when I tell you, at once –
   Very well then, come hither to me.'
Oh, look how he's trying in vain to stop crying,
   And ain't a good flogging a spree, my boys,
      and ain't Reggie Fane a good spree?

Oh, doesn't he try in his funk not to cry?
   But Reginald tried in vain,
For again Dr Church takes up a long birch,
   'Come here and kneel down, Reggie Fane,' he
      says, 'go down on the block, Reggie Fane.'

'Oh, please sir, no! I can't help, you know,
   If the birch makes me cry with the pain.'
'I'll have no crying here – not a cry – not a tear,
   So unbutton your trousers again, Reggie, and
      down with your trousers again.'

Now Reggie Fane kneels at his master's feet,
   With his backside naked again,
And the birch falls afresh on his red-wealed flesh –
   'Take that now, and that, young Fane,' it
      says, 'take that Master Reginald Fane.'

At the torture he feels from these fresh bloody weals,
   He bellows with all his young might,

And the blood lies in streaks on his bare nether
      cheeks,
  And ain't a good switching a sight, my boys?
      and ain't Reggie's bottom a sight?

And the blood runs in streams down his
      bottom, it seems,
  And the tears down his rosy face pouring;
And his naked hind part, how each stroke
      makes it smart,
  And how can the poor fellow stop roaring,
      my boys? and how *is* Reggie Fane to stop
      roaring?

He's half bit through his red lips, too,
  To stifle the cries of pain;
Well, I do think, I do, its hard lines on him, too –
  Hard lines on your brother Fred Fane, my
      boy, he's a plucky boy, too, Reggie Fane.

But it is a good lark – there, swish! again, hark –
  Swish! What a cut! What a cry!
Why he'll wear out the birch, and he'll tire out
      old Church;
  Well, rather Reggie than I, my boys, by Jove!
      I'm glad it's not I.

'Though your bottom be flayed, sir, I will be
    obeyed,'
  Thus Reginald's schoolmaster speaks,
And by dint of hard trying, at last he stops crying,
  And rises with burning cheeks, poor boy,
    with swollen and crimson cheeks.

The master stops – the birch rod drops,
  The boys still gaze in doubt;
But they see Reggie Fane with his clothes on
    again,
  As with tears in his eyes he goes out, poor boy, as
    with bottom well flayed he goes out.

Who ever yet saw a boy's bottom so raw
  As Fane's, now his flogging is done?
With his bottom all bloody, his face fair and
    ruddy,
  Oh! ain't a good flogging good fun, my boys,
    and ain't Reggie's flogging good fun.

Now Reggie Fane stands at his father's knee,
  Trembling and wincing with pain,
And its, 'Well, have you had a good flogging,
    my lad?
  Speak up now, Reggie Fane,' he says, 'speak
    up now, Reggie Fane.'

'Oh! I've had such a flogging dear father,' he says,
    'My bottom is so sore,
I shall never sit down again,
    My cuts will heal no more, father, my bum
        will heal no more.'

'The man that whipped your bottom, my boy,
    O blest may his right hand be;
And were you stripped in school and whipped?
    And did your schoolfellows see, Reggie, and
        did your schoolfellows see?'

'They stripped me bare in the high school hall,
    And all the boys were by;
And they saw the weals on my bare bottom,
    And laughed to hear me cry, father, when the
        birch had made me cry.'

'And did ye cry for pardon, Reggie?
    And did ye cry in vain?
And did ye cry as the birch came down?
    Oh! my boy, Reggie Fane,' he says, 'you bad
        boy, Reggie Fane.

'And did ye howl for mercy, Reggie?
    And did ye roar with pain?
And is it so bad to be whipped, my lad?

And must ye be whipped again, Reggie? and
   must ye taste birch twigs again?

'Had I been there while your bottom was bare,
   Oh! my boy, Reggie Fane,
For each cut of the birch from Dr Church,
   From me ye should have had twain, Reggie,
     I'd have given your bare breech twain.

'Had I here the rod in my hand, by God,
   Oh, my son, Reggie Fane,
You'd think no more of your switching before,
   When your breeches were down again, Reggie,
     when your bottom was tingling again.

'Had I here the school birch, like Dr Church,
   My young son, Reggie Fane,
I'd lay the lash on in such sharp fashion,
   I'd make you roar with the pain, Reggie,
     while your bottom could bear the pain.'

'There's no room for the birch on my bottom,
     father,
   My bottom is far too sore;
There's no room on my flesh, while these
     marks are fresh,
   For a single flesh wound more, father, for
     one cut or for one weal more.

'For the master's stripes were so hard, father,
　　And the twigs of birch so lithe,
That each twig and each bud as it fell drew
　　　　blood,
　　And oh! how it made me writhe, father. Oh,
　　　　sir, how it made me writhe.

'Each cut laid afresh on my quivering flesh,
　　Hurt the same tender part,
Each hard birchen bud drew a drop of my
　　　　blood,
　　And oh! how it made me smart, father, by
　　　　Jove! how it made me smart!

'And Dr Church, as he 'plied the birch,
　　Till he made the fragments fly,
Took aim with each blow where to hurt, you
　　　　know,
　　And oh! how he made me cry, father, how
　　　　the birch in his hand made me cry!

'And the other boys there, what a lot they were,
　　And that was worst of all,
They could see my bare bum, they could see
　　　　the blood come,
　　They could see the birch used on me fall, father,
　　　　they could look on and see the birch fall.

They could see the blood spin from the weals
    on my skin,
  They could see the birch fall and stand by;
And I heard them laughing, and knew they
    were chaffing,
  And they laughed if they saw me cry, father,
    and I heard and it made me cry.

'And the rods were there that he used on me.
  And he's promised to flog me again.'
'And as long as he's got 'em to use on your
    bottom,
  May he give you as good, Reggie Fane, my boy;
    may he flog you as well, Reggie Fane.'

ETONENSIS

A Boy's Flogging at Birchminster

'I say, Ernie, you've heard the news?' said Frank Anstruther.

Frank was a tall, fair school boy of sixteen; Ernest Elliot a blue-eyed, broad-shouldered, red-haired fellow of fourteen. Ernie was whipped about every other day; Frank about twice a week.

'No,' quoth Ernie, 'what's the row?'

'Why, young Aubrey Wilton's going to be swished at last; bet you he don't catch it, too – rather.'

'What! the little one? Baby Wilton? What a hell of a shame!'

'He is though, and he's in a blue funk. Why, three cuts would take the skin of his bottom, and they say he'll get two or three dozen – just for a taste. The new rods came in last night, more birch than two men could carry. Fred Wilton's in an awful stew; he says it'll half kill the young one.'

'By Jove,' said Ernie, 'I should think so; take his skin off? Why, the birch will cut him in half. I don't suppose he ever had a lash on his bottom in his life. Well, he was getting no end cockey and lazy, cribbing his work, and chaffing fellows because he knew they wouldn't lick him.'

Aubrey Wilton, just twelve, had been two months at the school and not had a flogging, a thing unheard of at

75

Birchminster. He was the prettiest boy there, with perfectly straight pure features, pale roses in the cheeks, thick brown eyebrows and eyelashes, light-brown curls that were golden and tawny or darker and warmer as sun or shade was on them, great brown eyes, like a wild animal's, and, unluckily, a skin too white and tender even for a girl. He was a quick, healthy boy, fresh and brave in his way, but never inured to pain or punished; spoilt by mother, brother, tutors, and schoolfellows; a nice enough boy by nature, and so handsome in mould of form and type of face that his beauty won upon all, and his natural grace of manner drew them close towards him. Older boys did his verses, kept off bullies, excused him fagging, and yet his own division did not hate or spite him. He was quick enough with a little help not to come to grief for some time, but his day was come now.

It wanted about twenty minutes to schooltime; the flogging began punctually at ten every morning, when the serious cases were cleared off, and such boys as had been solemnly complained of were publicly whipped by Dr Armstrong; there were usually also a dozen or so extempore floggings administered in the course of school hours.

'Who's going to be swished, Charlie?' said Harry Fane to Charlie Armstrong, the headmaster's second son. 'Apart from you, of course, Ernie,' turning to young Elliot, who grinned.

'Well,' said Charlie, 'I am for one, hang it; and your Major is, Anstruther; and Phil Acton and Percy Fielding and both Seytons and Reggie Shirley and, I think, Fred and Hugh and Tom Ainslie and Ned Wyat and Willie Goring and Chavering – not the old one, Arthur – and Harry Redfern.'

'I'm jolly glad he's in, too,' quoth Ernie; 'beast of a bully he is.'

'And young Lindsay – not Walter – and Reggie Arden, and two or three more,' said Charlie. 'My governor's in a jolly rage, he did nothing all night but look out the rods. I wish he'd take me last, when his arm's tired.'

'I'd rather come first, and have it over,' said Ernie, 'look at poor little Wilton, how he funks,' as that young gentleman approached with his cap over his eyes, very red and downcast.

'Never mind, Aubrey, boy, the second time it won't hurt you so much, and a fellow must begin some day. I was swished the first day I came for making too much row – didn't I blub, too?'

'I should think you did!' quoth Frank. 'I held you; you roared at each cut.'

'My pater said I wasn't to be spared if I did,' quoth Ernie, laughing. 'I had thirty lashes that first time; didn't it make me smart! But at last, when I was covered with red stripes and ridges of swollen and smarting flesh from the loins to the thighs, and my bottom was spotted with blood on both sides, and raw in half a dozen places, I was let go. I got up from the flogging block with my eyes full of tears, and almost as red in the face as I was behind; rubbed my bottom, dried my eyes and drew up my breeches, trying to swallow my sobs.

'While I was still buttoning up, and stopping at every button to rub my smarting skin, and before I had quite stopped sobbing and writhing, my cousin had taken my place. I was eager to see Reginald flogged; he was four years older, a big strong boy for his age! and I had always been told that he was oftener whipped at school than any boy of his standing.

77

He looked very sullen and savage as he began to loose his braces and let down his trousers before kneeling. The two boys in front whisked up his shirt, and his great stout bottom was exposed to the rod once more. I stood by and looked on, holding my breeches tight with both hands. I was very sore, and my fresh stripes tingled and smarted, but I thought less of my own flogging than Reggie's. There were marks of the rod on the fleshiest parts of his bottom; scars on either buttock, and bright red lines and furrows where the birch twigs had cut him hardest, all down the right side. But for these marks, the firm, white, solid cheeks of round, stout flesh, the smooth well-shaped loins, the large muscular thighs, the fair, delicate skin, and strong broad limbs were the model of a great, healthy handsome English boy in full bloom of growth, but the red streaks and lately healed scars told tales against Master Reggie. When he was adjusted on the block, and properly strapped up for whipping, the Doctor raised the rod again, and applied it sharply to Reginald's plump broad bottom.

'Reggie flinched; the rod fell again – rose – fell, and the boy's skin showed the marks of the fresh blows. At the fourth stroke blood was drawn in two places, and the whole bottom was one deep blush of red with bright thin stripes across it.

'There was a pause, Reggie's cheeks were red, but his posteriors were redder. He drew in his breath sharply, and bit his lips. The Doctor looked at his birch before he applied it again; it was much worn and frayed, the fresh twigs and green sappy buds had all been spent on my bottom. I felt them still. He gave it to one of the boys in waiting, who handed him a large fresh birch with long pliant green twigs, thin enough to sting well and stout enough to hold out without breaking till the bottom of the boy punished was all over blood. He tried it first with a sharp short swish in the air, then raised it high – swung it out at arm's length, and brought it down with all his might. It cut through the air with a loud hissing sound, and fell right on the boy's already tender bottom with a great smack.

'Reginald roared; the rod caught him across again, and raised a fresh bloody ridge of smarting flesh –

' "Oh, sir," Reggie cried out – swish!

' "Oh! sir, oh!" – swish.

'Reggie took the eighth cut without a word. Swish! The ninth cut was such a sharp one that the fresh twigs bent round with the force of the stroke, but Reggie hardly winced. Swish! The tenth cut drew a little stream of blood, and there were fresh wounds in the place of the old scars, and new bloody stripes where the boy's flesh was whole and unwounded before.

'Reginald writhed. Swish! Still not a word. Reggie had made up his mind. Swish! One more, the boy thought, and the flogging would be over. Swish! it was a sharp cut, and it was not the last. Swish! Reggie gave in at the fourteenth stroke, and roared with agony. Swish! The birch was sharper than ever, and the cry louder than before –

' "Oh, sir, please!" – Swish!

'The last cut left poor Reginald's bare bottom covered with blood. He rose from the block crying and sobbing like a child. It was not every day that a boy got so severe a flogging, and it made him so tame and gentle that he was quite kind to me all that day, and helped me to pick out the broken bits of birch that were sticking in my flesh.'

Whipping of Boadicea

Prasutagus, King of the Iceni, and husband to Boadicea, having no son to inherit his dominions, bequeathed his immense treasures to the Emperor of the Romans and his two daughters as joint heirs, hoping by that means to procure a powerful protector for his daughters; but he was fatally deceived. Catus Decianus, the procurator, a monster of vice, avarice and injustice, seized upon the whole, and deprived the daughters of their inheritance, which Boadicea loudly exclaimed against; Catus ordered her to be publicly whipped, and suffered the soldiers to violate the chastity of her two daughters. These inhuman proceedings roused Boadicea to vengeance, and the author of these shocking acts of brutality would have been destined for destruction had he not made his escape. She put as many as seventy thousand Romans to the sword and laid three cities in ashes before being defeated by Suetonius in AD 61, whereupon she poisoned herself.

Whipping as a Punishment for Adultery

Formerly in Germany the husband of an adulteress was allowed to assemble her relations, and in their presence to cut off her hair, strip her naked, turn her out of his house and whip her from one end of the village to the other. A woman thus publicly exposed could never wipe away the stain of so foul an infamy; the most circumspect behaviour could never call back her lost character; nor could any motive ever prevail on another to marry her, though youth, beauty and fortune, with every other advantage, combined to allure them.

ALEXANDER'S *History of Women*

Woman Publicly Whipped for being
Too Fruitful

Being the speech of Miss Polly Baker's – delivered before a court of judicature, Connecticut, in New England, upon her being prosecuted the fifth time for having a bastard child – which influenced the court to dispense with her punishment and induced one of her judges to marry her the next day; by him she had another fifteen children.

May it please the honourable bench to indulge me in a few words. I am a poor unhappy woman, who has no money to fee lawyers to plead for me, being hard put to it to get a tolerable living. I shall not trouble your honours with a long speech, for I have not the presumption to expect that you may, by any means, be prevailed on to deviate in your sentence from the law in my favour. All I humbly hope is that your honours would charitably move the governor's goodness on my behalf, that my fine may be remitted. This is the fifth time, gentlemen, that I have been dragged before your court on the same account: twice I have paid heavy fines, and twice I have been publicly whipped for want of money to pay those fines. This may have been agreeable to the laws, and I do not dispute it; but since laws are sometimes unreasonable in themselves, and therefore re-pealed, and others bear too hard on the subject in particular instances, and therefore there is left a power somewhat to dispense with the execution of them, I take the liberty to say, that I think this law by which I am punished is both unreasonable in itself, and particularly severe with regard to me, who have always lived an inoffensive life in the neighbourhood where I was born, and defy my enemies (if I have any) to say I ever wronged man, woman or child.

Abstracted from the law, I cannot conceive, may it please your honours, what the nature of my offence is. I have brought five fine children into the world at the risk of my life. I have maintained them well by my own industry, without burdening the township; and would have done it better if it had not been for the heavy charges and fines I have paid.

Can it be a crime (in the nature of things, I mean) to add to the number of the king's subjects, in a new country that really wants people?

I own I should think it a praiseworthy, rather than a punishable action.

I have debauched no other woman's husband, nor enticed any youth; these things I never was charged with, nor has anyone the least cause of complaint against me, unless, perhaps, the minister or justice, because I have had children without being married, by which they have missed a wedding fee.

But can this be a fault of mine? I appeal to your honours, what you are pleased to allow. I don't want sense, but that I am stupefied to the last degree, not to prefer the honourable state of wedlock to the condition I have lived in. I always was, and still am, willing to enter into it, and doubt not my behaving well in it, having all the industry, frugality, fertility, and skill in economy appertaining to a good wife's character.

I defy any person to say I ever refused an offer of that sort; on the contrary, I readily consented to the only proposal of marriage that ever was made me, which was when I was a virgin, but too easily confided in the person's sincerity that made it. I unhappily lost my own honour by trusting to his; for he got me with child and then forsook me.

That very person you all know. He is now become a magistrate of this country; and I had hopes he would have appeared this day on the bench, and have endeavoured to moderate the court in my favour, then I should have scorned to have mentioned it, but I now must complain of it as unjust and unequal, that my betrayer and undoer, the first cause of all my faults and miscarriages (if they must be deemed such), should be advanced to honour and power in the government that punishes my misfortunes with stripes and infamy.

You say precepts of religion are violated by my transgressions. If mine is a religious offence, leave it to religious punishments. You have already excluded me from the comforts of your church communion; is not that sufficient? You believe I have offended heaven, and must suffer eternal fire; will not that be sufficient? What need is there then of your additional fines and whippings. I own I do not think as you do; for if I thought what you call a sin was really such, I could not presumptuously commit it. But how can it be believed that Heaven is angry at my having children, when to the little done by me towards it, God has been pleased to add his divine skill and admirable workmanship in the formation of their bodies, and crowned it by finishing them with rational and immortal souls.

Forgive me, gentlemen, if I talk a little extravagantly on these matters. I am no divine; but if you, gentlemen, must be making laws, do not turn natural and useful actions into crimes by your prohibitions, but take into your wise consideration the great and growing numbers of bachelors in the country, many of whom, from the mean fear of the expenses of a family, have never sincerely and honourably courted a woman in their lives; and by their manner of living, leave unproduced (which is little better than murder) hundreds of their posterity to the thousandth generation.

Is this not a greater offence to the public good than mine? Compel them then by law either to marriage or to pay double the fine of fornication every year.

What must poor young women do whom custom hath forbade to solicit the men, and who cannot force themselves upon husbands, when the law takes no care to provide them any, and severely punishes them if they do their duty without them, the duty of the first and great command of nature's God – increase and multiply? A duty from the steady performance of which nothing has been able to deter me, but for its sake I have hazarded the loss of the public esteem, and have frequently endured public disgrace and punishment; and therefore ought, in my humble opinion, instead of a whipping, to have a statue erected to my memory.

7 MARCH 1771

85

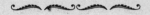

Whipping as a Punishment in Russia

The knute is a most barbarous punishment in Russia.

Olearious gives a description of the manner in which he saw it inflicted on eight men and one woman, only for selling brandy and tobacco without a licence.

The executioner's man, after stripping them down to the waist, tied their feet, and took one at a time upon his back.

The executioner stood at three paces' distance with a bull's pizzle, to the end of which were fastened three thongs of untanned elk's skin, with which, springing forward, whenever he struck the blood gushed out at every blow.

The men had each twenty-five or twenty-six lashes. The woman, though only sixteen, fainted away.

After their backs were thus dreadfully mangled, they were tied together two and two, and those who had sold tobacco had a little of it, and those who had sold brandy had a little bottle put about their necks, and then they were whipped through the city of St Petersburg for about a mile and a half, and then brought back to the place of their first punishment and dismissed.

According to M. de la Motreye, this is what is termed the moderate knute; for when the sentence orders it between the moderate and severe, the executioner takes off pieces of flesh at every stroke; and when it is ordered to be given with the utmost severity, the executioner striking the flank under the ribs, cuts the flesh to the very bowels.

It is no wonder that many die of this cruel and inhuman punishment.

NEWBURY'S *Account of Russia*

Extracts from Buckle's Tract

Miss L—, another votary to birch-discipline was the daughter of a clergyman who kept a school at —. Her mother dying when she was about thirteen, her father, as she was very clever, and very tall for her age, gave her the care of her sisters; as they were very giddy, she got leave from her father to whip them. She grew so fond of the birch, that she found means to get other young girls to instruct and on them she administered, very often, the rod. Her father dying when she was about two-and-twenty, she came to town, opened a young ladies' boarding-school, and in a few years got a very large school. She then gave free rein to her favourite passion, whipping sometimes a dozen girls a day. As she was an experienced hand at whipping, she seldom dismissed them till their posteriors and thighs were as red as scarlet. Her pleasure was to cut them, and generally whipped till the blood would come. She continued that practice till they were at least fifteen. Many mothers approved of her conduct very much. She had a closet full of birch-rods of different-sizes, curiously bound with ribbons of different colours.

She took a singular pleasure in choosing the long slender twigs of the birch with buds on them, and binding them up in rods; she never used the rod twice, nor any birch but that was cut lately. The smell of new birch raised in her the most pleasing sensation. After she had whipped a girl, she always made her wear the rod in her bosom as a nosegay for two or three hours.

The Hon. Mr S—, at the age of seventeen, had a beautiful sister a year younger than him. She married Lord —. Their father and mother being dead, they lived with an old aunt. Mr S. was then at Oxford, but came to town very often. He had taken notice of his sister whipping very often a pretty cousin, a girl about ten years old, who was under her care. One day as he was reading in his sister's room a French book about women being fond of whipping, which he had found in her closet, he heard her coming with her cousin, who was then crying; suspecting she was going to whip her, he hid himself behind the curtain of the bed. He was not mistaken; his sister immediately entered with a good birch-rod in her hand. Petticoats, &c., were all soon removed. After whipping her very severely, and lecturing her all the time, as an experienced schoolmistress, she sent her downstairs, and soon went herself as if nothing had happened.

Mr D— declared to a friend of his that he never saw anything so pretty, his sister being dressed that day all in white, with a large pink sash round her waist; her hair, which was not yet turned up, wantonly flowing on her snowy bosom, which was heaving all the time; a pretty hat on one side of the head, full of large white ostrich feathers, and a beautiful bouquet of a most enormous size, made of moss-roses, carnations, pinks intermixed with large bunches of myrtle, jessamy and mignionette, which she wore on the left side, up to the ear. The exquisite perfume of it excited in him such agreeable sensations that after that he could never abide his sister or any young lady of his acquaintance without just such a monstrous corsage. The waving of the feathers, the shaking of the flowers of the nosegay, the sound of the birch, and especially the exquisite perfume which the bouquet exhaled, had such an effect on him that he remained for an hour in a sort of ecstasy. He had a garden entirely laid out with the most beautiful sweet flowers imaginable. He used to send out of it to his female acquaintance large bouquets that he might have the pleasure of seeing them dress well at the public places where he knew he would meet with them; to tie himself a nosegay for the bosom of a lady was a delight to him. His seeing one day a lady at the Pantheon, the beautiful Miss W—, with a most enormous side-bouquet, whose pretty face could scarce be seen among the flowers, he fell in love with her, and married her about a month after; she was but fourteen then, and just out of school.

On the continent, where whipping is so fashionable, it is one of the chief amusements of nuns, for they not only whip one another for their pleasure, but will whip with shocking

birch-rods their boarders, with so much severity that sometimes some of them are obliged to keep their beds for two or
three days; this is a fact, and many young ladies who have
been educated there would assert it. I was always surprised
not to meet with any book which would lay open the
incontinency of the nuns; for some nuns take as much
pleasure in whipping a pretty girl, with the help of a certain
curious instrument, as they would almost to sleep with a
man, and have almost the same pleasure.

A duchess in Paris, who has tasted of this felicity from the
hands of a vast number of ladies of her own complexion, took
an uncommon liking to a beautiful West-Indian negro
woman, who had been brought to Paris by a naval officer,
from whom she was purchased at an high price by her for
this purpose. As soon as she was in possession of her she
spared no expense in educating her, and clothed her in the
most elegant manner. When she fancied she was polished at
all points for her purpose she broke the matter to her, and,
with the assistance of a number of books and prints on the
subject, instructed her perfectly. She often declared to a
female confidante, nothing could equal the pleasure she felt
when this lovely negro stripped her or took her out of bed; to
feel her velvet hands run over her thighs and posteriors when
she was settling on her knees, and, immediately after, to feel
the rod smartly exercised by her, was to her the height of
human pleasure. This woman, strange as it may appear, had
such an ascendancy over this illustrious lady, that she was in
a short while mistress of her affection and fortune. I have

been well assured a gentleman now in London has a pretty negro maidservant, and his greatest delight is to see her whip his children.

Cruel Whipping by a Young Lady

A young officer, of liberal education and genteel connections, being in the West Indies with his regiment, fell in love with a young lady, the daughter of a respectable planter, and offered her his hand, which, with the consent of her parents, she accepted.

The day of marriage was accordingly fixed, and everything previously settled. Early in the morning of this wished-for day, the impatient youth hurried to his mistress's apartment, that, out of a frolic, he might surprise her in bed. On entering it he found she was up, and he was charmed with the neat and elegant appearance of everything around; every part of the apartment was decked and perfumed with garlands and festoons of various coloured flowers.

He enquired of a female slave where her young mistress was, and upon her pointing to the back area of the house, he flew thither on the wings of love! But what was his astonishment to behold the charmer of his soul very coolly and deliberately superintending the punishment of a little mulatto girl, who was suspended by one hand while a negro whipped her.

Her piercing cries sufficiently testified the agony she endured, and sank deep in the heart of the thunderstruck lover, who stood aghast, not offering to advance.

At length he recollected himself, and springing back abruptly, drew out a slip of paper, and hastily pencilled upon it an eternal adieu!

Letter to the Editor on Flagellation in Mixed Boarding Schools

SIR – A few years ago, at a free school near Lincoln's Inn Fields, where boys and girls were taught under the same roof, flogging, with a birch rod, was daily practised as a punishment.

At this school I saw thirty boys flogged one morning. A gang of them every evening had sallied forth and had stolen anything within their reach, such as bell pulls, brass knobs, &c., &c. A few were detected, and they implicated the others; five girls were also with them. They were all severely flogged – girls as well.

But on common occasions, whenever a boy was horsed, his outcry brought the curious girls to a window, which commanded a full view of the subsequent operation. These young ladies were occasionally subject to the same sort of punishment, but not exposed, I believe, to the boys' gaze;

but as it was well known when the infliction was taking place, it was observed by the boys as curious that the master was generally absent from the schoolroom during the time, but whether to *assist* or *instruct* the mistress could only be surmised. It was certain that often when the latter visited the master during schooltime for any purpose, the birch was brought forth, and a boy's bottom soon found to practise upon, for the advantage of the instruction it afforded the lady in search of knowledge. On such occasions, her pupils, being left to themselves, used to enjoy the distant prospect also.

This sort of intercourse was, however, at last broken up when a big, unruly Irish girl, who had been slightly punished and resented it, knocked down the mistress and called her a whore in plain terms.

Some of the girls ran to the master, who, upon his arrival, without any ceremony, after extricating the lady, laid the girl across a form and broke a rod to pieces on her crimsoned bottom. He was admonished on the score of propriety not to repeat such a flogging on female pupils – and so it ended.

At the same school the late Earl of Portsmouth, who was (for certain gratifying personal objects) a very large benefactor, and who, in consequence, was allowed to do as he pleased (as may be seen in the lunacy examination before the commissioners), used to amuse himself by attending the boys' school and whipping them at his discretion. He would also insist upon the mistress whipping any girl he might point out, and this was done to conciliate him – the party punished receiving some equivalent reward afterwards, while the laceration was never very great. From the fact of presents known to have been sent from his earlship, little doubt exists that he was in the habit of enjoying 'visual prospects' at least.

It is also stated that the earl's lady and her butler used to turn the tables on his earlship, by the latter whipping his posteriors with a rod or whip, while the former held up his shirt, and that she always slept with such an instrument under her pillow.

Yours &c.,

CASTIGATOR

The late Sir Eyre Coote was, it is well known, fond of this amusement. He was detected at Christ's Hospital whipping the boys, and being also whipped himself – one of the nurses going into the room where he lay exposed. A pamphlet was published at the time explaining the particulars, but it was bought up by his family, and it is not now to be found.

WORDSWORTH DISTRIBUTION

Great Britain and Ireland
Wordsworth Editions Limited
Cumberland House, Crib Street
Ware, Hertfordshire SG12 9ET
Telephone 01920 465 167
Fax 01920 462 267

USA, Canada and Mexico
Universal Sales & Marketing Inc
230 Fifth Avenue, Suite 1212
New York, NY 10001, USA
Telephone 212-481-3500
Fax 212-481-3534

Italy
Magis Books SRL
Via Raffaello 31c
Zona ind Mancasale
42100 Reggio Emilia, Italy
Telephone 0522-920999
Fax 0522-920666

**Germany, Austria and
Switzerland**
Swan Buch-Marketing GmbH
Goldscheuerstrabe 16
D-7640 Kehl am Rhein, Germany

Portugal
International Publishing
Services Limited
Rua da Cruz da Carreira, 4B
1100 Lisboa
Telephone 01-570051
Fax 01-352-2066

Spain
Ribera Libros S L
Poligono Martiartu, Calle 1, no 6
48480 Arrigorriaga, Vizcaya
Tel. 34-4-671-3607 (Almacen)
Tel. 34-4-441-8787 (Libreria)
Fax 34-4-671-3608 (Almacen)
Fax 34-4-4418029 (Libreria)

Wordsworth Classic Erotica

ANONYMOUS
*The Autobiography
of a Flea*

Blue Velvet

Eveline

Frank and I

First Training

A Night in a Moorish Harem

The Pearl

Randiana

The Romance of Lust

Sadopaideia

Suburban Souls

Teleny

The Whippingham Papers

GUILLAUME APOLLINAIRE
*The Amorous Exploits of
a Young Rakehell*

GIOVANNI BOCCACCIO
*Selections from
The Decameron*

JOHN CLELAND
*Memoirs of a Woman of
Pleasure – Fanny Hill*

SHEIKH NEFZAOUI
The Perfumed Garden
TRANSLATED BY
SIR RICHARD BURTON

PAULINE REAGE
The Story of O

EDWARD SELLON
The New Epicurean

SMITHERS AND BURTON
Priapaia

VARIOUS
*The Olympia Reader –
Volume One*
*The Olympia Reader –
Volume Two*

VATSYAYANA
The Kama Sutra
TRANSLATED BY
SIR RICHARD BURTON &
F. F. ARBUTHNOT

'WALTER'
My Secret Life – Volume One
My Secret Life – Volume Two

LI YU
The Carnal Prayer Mat